WINGS *from* *the* WIND

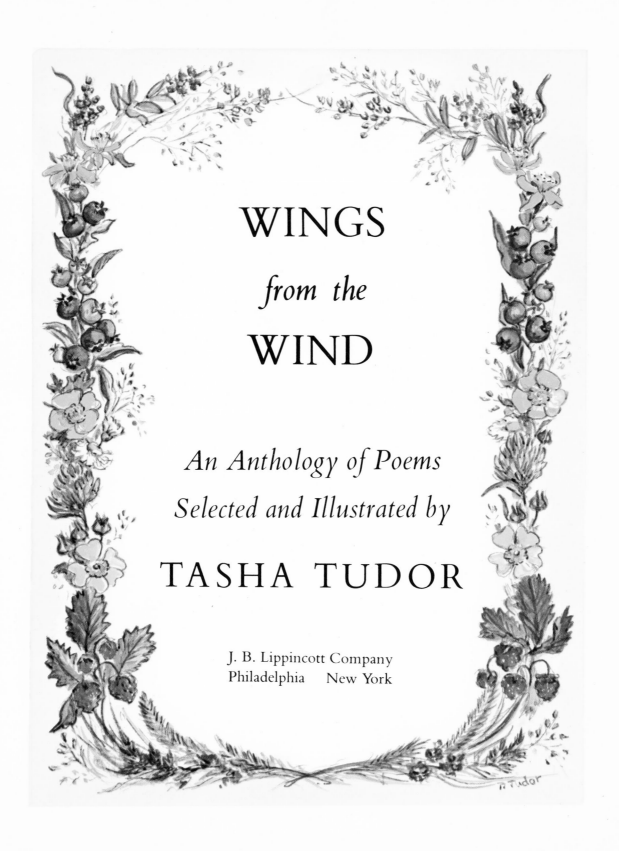

WINGS

from the

WIND

An Anthology of Poems

Selected and Illustrated by

TASHA TUDOR

J. B. Lippincott Company
Philadelphia   New York

To Eunice Blake

ACKNOWLEDGMENTS

Thanks go to the following publishers, agents and individuals for their kind permission to reprint material copyrighted or controlled by them:

Brandt & Brandt for "A Nonsense Song" from SELECTED WORKS OF STEPHEN VINCENT BENÉT, published by Holt, Rinehart and Winston, Inc.; copyright, 1925, by Stephen Vincent Benét; copyright renewed, 1953, by Rosemary Carr Benét. For "Captain Kidd" from A BOOK OF AMERICANS by Rosemary and Stephen Vincent Benét, published by Holt, Rinehart and Winston, Inc.; copyright, 1933, by Rosemary and Stephen Vincent Benét; copyright renewed, 1961, by Rosemary Carr Benét.

Doubleday & Company, Inc. for "General Store" from TAXIS AND TOADSTOOLS by Rachel Field. Copyright, 1926, by Rachel Field.

E. P. Dutton & Co., the Executors of the H. J. Cape Estate, and Jonathan Cape Limited for "Green Rain," "A Hawthorn Berry," "Starlings," and "The Water Ousel" by Mary Webb from the book, POEMS AND THE SPRING OF JOY. Copyright, 1929, by E. P. Dutton & Co., Inc. Renewal, 1957, by Jonathan Cape.

Harcourt, Brace & World, Inc. for "Primer Lesson" from SLABS OF THE SUNBURNT WEST by Carl Sandburg. Copyright, 1922, by Harcourt, Brace & World, Inc.; copyright, 1950, by Carl Sandburg.

CONTENTS

Thoughts

MATIN SONG

Pack, clouds, away! and welcome, day!
    With night we banish sorrow.
Sweet air, blow soft; mount, lark, aloft
    To give my Love good-morrow!
Wings from the wind to please her mind,
    Notes from the lark I'll borrow:
Bird, prune thy wing! nightingale, sing!
      To give my Love good-morrow!
      To give my Love good-morrow!
      Notes from them all I'll borrow.

Wake from thy nest, robin red-breast!
    Sing, birds, in every furrow!
And from each bill let music shrill
    Give my fair Love good-morrow!
Blackbird and thrush in every bush,
    Stare, linnet, and cocksparrow,
You pretty elves, among yourselves
    Sing my fair Love good-morrow!
      To give my Love good-morrow!
      Sing, birds, in every furrow!

THOMAS HEYWOOD

11

He came all so still
    Where his mother was,
As dew in April
    That falleth on the grass.

He came all so still
    To his mother's bower,
As dew in April
    That falleth on the flower.

He came all so still
    Where his mother lay,
As dew in April
    That falleth on the spray.

ANONYMOUS

INFANT JOY

"I have no name;
I am but two days old."
What shall I call thee?
"I happy am,
Joy is my name."
Sweet joy befall thee!

Pretty joy!
Sweet joy, but two days old.
Sweet joy I call thee;
Thou dost smile,
I sing the while;
Sweet joy befall thee!

WILLIAM BLAKE

13

Little lad, little lad,
    Where were you born?
Far off in Lancashire,
    Under a thorn,
Where they sup butter-milk
    With a ram's horn;
And a pumpkin scoop'd
    With a yellow rim,
Is the bonny bowl
    They breakfast in.

MOTHER GOOSE

How many miles to Babylon?
Three-score and ten.
Can I get there by candlelight?
Yes, and back again.
If your heels are nimble and light,
You may get there by candlelight.

MOTHER GOOSE

14

When I was a little boy
    My mammy kept me in,
But now I am a great boy
    I'm fit to serve the king;
I can hand a musket,
    And I can smoke a pipe,
And I can kiss a bonny girl
    At twelve o'clock at night.

                    MOTHER GOOSE

Intery, mintery, cutery corn,
Apple seed and apple thorn;
Wire, briar, limber lock,
Three geese in a flock,
One flew east and one flew west
And one flew over the goose's nest.

                    MOTHER GOOSE

Star light, star bright,
First star I've seen tonight,
I wish I may, I wish I might
Get the wish I wish tonight.

MOTHER GOOSE

Load of hay
Load of hay
Make a wish
And turn away.

MOTHER GOOSE

TWELFTH NIGHT

Here's to thee, old apple tree,
Whence thou may'st bud
And whence thou may'st blow,
And whence thou may'st bear apples enow;
Hats full and caps full,
Bushels full and sacks full,
And our pockets full too.

MOTHER GOOSE

17

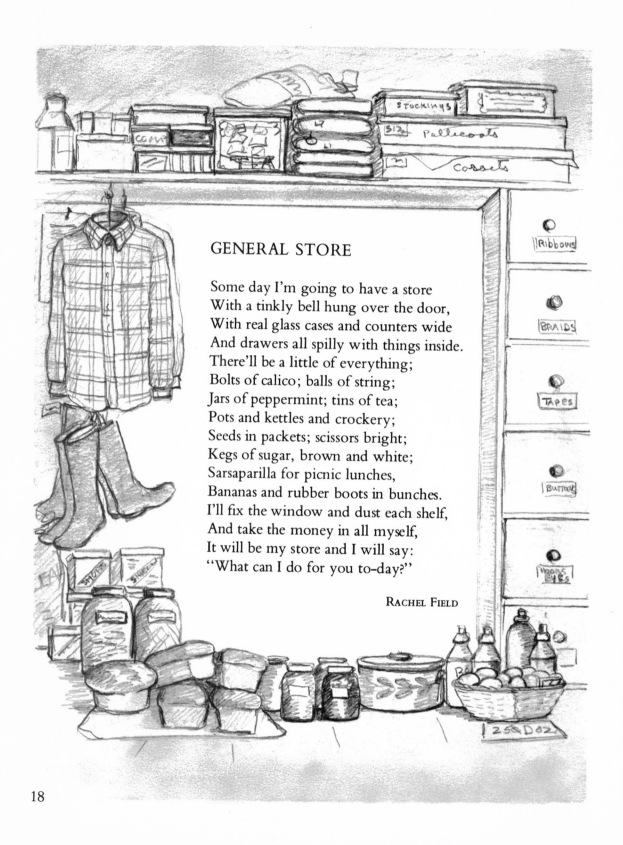

GENERAL STORE

Some day I'm going to have a store
With a tinkly bell hung over the door,
With real glass cases and counters wide
And drawers all spilly with things inside.
There'll be a little of everything;
Bolts of calico; balls of string;
Jars of peppermint; tins of tea;
Pots and kettles and crockery;
Seeds in packets; scissors bright;
Kegs of sugar, brown and white;
Sarsaparilla for picnic lunches,
Bananas and rubber boots in bunches.
I'll fix the window and dust each shelf,
And take the money in all myself,
It will be my store and I will say:
"What can I do for you to-day?"

RACHEL FIELD

THE CHILDREN'S HOUR

Between the dark and the daylight,
    When the night is beginning to lower,
Comes a pause in the day's occupations
    That is known as the Children's Hour.

I hear in the chamber above me
    The patter of little feet,
The sound of a door that is opened,
    And voices soft and sweet.

From my study I see in the lamplight,
    Descending the broad hall stair,
Grave Alice and laughing Allegra,
    And Edith with golden hair.

A whisper, and then a silence:
    Yet I know by their merry eyes
They are plotting and planning together
    To take me by surprise.

A sudden rush from the stairway,
    A sudden raid from the hall!
By three doors left unguarded
    They enter my castle wall!

They climb up into my turret
    O'er the arms and back of my chair;
If I try to escape, they surround me;
    They seem to be everywhere.

They almost devour me with kisses,
    Their arms about me entwine,
Till I think of the Bishop of Bingen
    In his Mouse-Tower on the Rhine!

Do you think, O blue-eyed banditti,
    Because you have scaled the wall,
Such an old mustache as I am
    Is not a match for you all!

I have you fast in my fortress,
    And will not let you depart,
But put you down into the dungeon
    In the round-tower of my heart.

And there will I keep you forever,
    Yes, forever and a day,
Till the walls shall crumble to ruin,
    And moulder in dust away!

HENRY WADSWORTH LONGFELLOW

THE VILLAGE BLACKSMITH

Under a spreading chestnut-tree
The village smithy stands;
The smith, a mighty man is he,
With large and sinewy hands;
And the muscles of his brawny arms
Are strong as iron bands.

His hair is crisp, and black, and long,
His face is like the tan;
His brow is wet with honest sweat,
He earns whate'er he can,
And looks the whole world in the face,
For he owes not any man.

Week in, week out, from morn till night,
You can hear his bellows blow;
You can hear him swing his heavy sledge,
With measured beat and slow,
Like a sexton ringing the village bell,
When the evening sun is low.

And children coming home from school
Look in at the open door;
They love to see the flaming forge,
And hear the bellows roar,
And catch the burning sparks that fly
Like chaff from a threshing-floor.

He goes on Sunday to the church,
And sits among his boys;
He hears the parson pray and preach,
He hears his daughter's voice,
Singing in the village choir,
And it makes his heart rejoice.

It sounds to him like her mother's voice,
Singing in Paradise!
He needs must think of her once more,
How in the grave she lies;
And with his hard, rough hand he wipes
A tear out of his eyes.

Toiling—rejoicing—sorrowing,
Onward through life he goes;
Each morning sees some task begin,
Each evening sees it close;
Something attempted, something done,
Has earned a night's repose.

Thanks, thanks to thee, my worthy friend,
For the lesson thou has taught!
Thus at the flaming forge of life
Our fortunes must be wrought;
Thus on its sounding anvil shaped
Each burning deed and thought!

HENRY WADSWORTH LONGFELLOW

WINDY NIGHTS

Whenever the moon and stars are set,
    Whenever the wind is high,
All night long in the dark and wet,
    A man goes riding by.
Late in the night when the fires are out,
Why does he gallop and gallop about?

Whenever the trees are crying aloud,
    And ships are tossed at sea,
By, on the highway, low and loud,
    By at the gallop goes he.
By at the gallop he goes, and then
By he comes back at the gallop again.

ROBERT LOUIS STEVENSON

KEEPSAKE MILL

Over the borders, a sin without pardon,
　　Breaking the branches and crawling below,
Out through the breach in the wall of the garden,
　　Down by the banks of the river, we go.

Here is the mill with the humming of thunder,
　　Here is the weir with the wonder of foam,
Here is the sluice with the race running under—
　　Marvelous places, though handy to home!

Sounds of the village grow stiller and stiller,
　　Stiller the note of the birds on the hill;
Dusty and dim are the eyes of the miller,
　　Deaf are his ears with the moil of the mill.

Years may go by, and the wheel in the river
    Wheel as it wheels for us, children, to-day,
Wheel and keep roaring and foaming for ever
    Long after all of the boys are away.

Home from the Indies and home from the ocean,
    Heroes and soldiers we all shall come home;
Still we shall find the old mill wheel in motion,
    Turning and churning that river to foam.

You with the bean that I gave when we quarreled,
    I with your marble of Saturday last,
Honored and old and all gaily appareled,
    Here we shall meet and remember the past.

ROBERT LOUIS STEVENSON

WEATHERS

This is the weather the cuckoo likes,
    And so do I;
When showers betumble the chestnut spikes,
    And nestlings fly;
And the little brown nightingale bills his best,
    And they sit outside at "The Travellers' Rest."
And maids come forth sprig-muslin drest,
And citizens dream of the south and west,
    And so do I.

This is the weather the shepherd shuns,
    And so do I;
When beeches drip in browns and duns,
    And thresh, and ply;
And hill-hid tides throb, throe on throe,
And meadow rivulets overflow,
And drops on gate-bars hang in a row,
And rooks in families homeward go,
    And so do I.

THOMAS HARDY

THE CONCORD HYMN

By the rude bridge that arched the flood,
Their flag to April's breeze unfurled,
Here once the embattled farmers stood,
And fired the shot heard round the world.

The foe long since in silence slept;
Alike the conqueror silent sleeps;
And Time the ruined bridge has swept
Down the dark stream which seaward creeps.

On this green bank, by this soft stream,
We set today a votive stone;
That memory may their dead redeem,
When, like our sires, our sons are gone.

Spirit, that made those spirits dare
To die, and leave their children free,
Bid Time and Nature gently spare
The shaft we raise to them and thee.

RALPH WALDO EMERSON

A WANDERER'S SONG

A wind's in the heart of me, a fire's in my heels,
I am tired of brick and stone and rumbling wagon-wheels;
I hunger for the sea's edge, the limits of the land,
Where the wild old Atlantic is shouting on the sand.

Oh, I'll be going, leaving the noises of the street,
To where a lifting foresail-foot is yanking at the sheet;
To a windy, tossing anchorage where yawls and ketches
          ride,
Oh, I'll be going, going, until I meet the tide.

And first I'll hear the sea-wind, the mewing of the gulls,
The clucking, sucking of the sea about the rusty hulls,
The songs at the capstan in the hooker warping out,
And then the heart of me'll know I'm there or thereabout.

Oh, I am tired of brick and stone, the heart of me is sick,
For windy green, unquiet sea, the realm of Moby Dick;
And I'll be going, going, from the roaring of the wheels,
For a wind's in the heart of me, a fire's in my heels.

JOHN MASEFIELD

32

OLD SHIPS

There is a memory stays upon old ships,
    A weightless cargo in the musty hold,—
Of bright lagoons and prow-caressing lips,
    Of stormy midnights,—and a tale untold.
They have remembered islands in the dawn.
    And windy capes that tried their slender spars,
And tortuous channels where their keels have gone,
    And calm blue nights of stillness and the stars.

Ah, never think that ships forget a shore,
    Or bitter seas, or winds that made them wise;
There is a dream upon them, evermore;
    And there be some who say that sunk ships rise
To seek familiar harbors in the night,
Blowing in mists, their spectral sails like light.

DAVID MORTON

CAPTAIN KIDD
1650?-1701

This person in the gaudy clothes
Is worthy Captain Kidd.
They say he never buried gold.
I think, perhaps, he did.

They say it's all a story that
His favorite little song
Was "Make these lubbers walk the plank!"
I think, perhaps, they're wrong.

They say he never pirated
Beneath the Skull-and-Bones.
He merely traveled for his health
And spoke in soothing tones.
In fact, you'll read in nearly all
The newer history books
That he was mild as cottage cheese
—But I don't like his looks!

STEPHEN VINCENT BENÉT

PRIMER LESSON

Look out how you use proud words.
When you let proud words go, it is not
    easy to call them back.
They wear long boots, hard boots;
    they walk off proud; they can't
    hear you calling—
Look out how you use proud words.

CARL SANDBURG

LEISURE

What is this life if, full of care,
We have no time to stand and stare.

No time to stand beneath the boughs
And stare as long as sheep or cows.

No time to see, when woods we pass,
Where squirrels hide their nuts in grass.

No time to see, in broad daylight,
Streams full of stars, like stars at night.

No time to turn at Beauty's glance,
And watch her feet, how they can dance.

No time to wait till her mouth can
Enrich that smile her eyes began.

A poor life this if, full of care,
We have no time to stand and stare.

WILLIAM HENRY DAVIES

MEETING AT NIGHT

The gray sea and the long black land;
And the yellow half-moon large and low;
And the startled little waves that leap
In fiery ringlets from their sleep,
As I gain the cove with pushing prow,
And quench its speed i' the slushy sand.

Then a mile of warm sea-scented beach;
Three fields to cross till a farm appears;
A tap at the pane, the quick sharp scratch
And blue spurt of a lighted match,
And a voice less loud, through its joys and fears,
Than the two hearts beating each to each!

ROBERT BROWNING

PORTRAIT BY A NEIGHBOR

Before she has her floor swept
    Or her dishes done,
Any day you'll find her
    A-sunning in the sun!

It's long after midnight
    Her key's in the lock,
And you never see her chimney smoke
    Till past ten o'clock!

She digs in her garden
    With a shovel and a spoon,
She weeds her lazy lettuce
    By the light of the moon.

She walks up the walk
    Like a woman in a dream,
She forgets she borrowed butter
    And pays you back cream!

Her lawn looks like a meadow,
    And if she mows the place
She leaves the clover standing
    And the Queen Anne's lace!

EDNA ST. VINCENT MILLAY

DUST OF SNOW

The way a crow
Shook down on me
The dust of snow
From a hemlock tree

Has given my heart
A change of mood
And saved some part
Of a day I had rued.

ROBERT FROST

SAY NOT

Say not, the struggle nought availeth,
　　The labor and the wounds are vain,
The enemy faints not, nor faileth,
　　And as things have been they remain.

If hopes were dupes, fears may be liars;
　　It may be, in yon smoke concealed,
Your comrades chase e'en now the fliers,
　　And, but for you, possess the field.

For while the tired waves, vainly breaking,
　　Seem here no painful inch to gain,
Far back, through creeks and inlets making,
　　Comes silent, flooding in, the main.

And not by eastern windows only,
　　When daylight comes, comes in the light;
In front, the sun climbs slow, how slowly!
　　But westward, look, the land is bright!

A. H. CLOUGH

Yet Ah, that Spring should vanish with the Rose!
That Youth's sweet-scented manuscript should close!
The Nightingale that in the branches sang,
Ah whence, and whither flown again, who knows?

OMAR KHAYYAM

As the Earth Turns

GOD'S WORLD

O World, I cannot hold thee close enough!
    Thy winds, thy wide grey skies!
    Thy mists that roll and rise!
Thy woods, this autumn day, that ache and sag
And all but cry with color! That gaunt crag
To crush! To lift the lean of that black bluff!
World, World, I cannot get thee close enough!

Long have I known a glory in it all,
        But never knew I this;
        Here such a passion is
As stretcheth me apart. Lord, I do fear
Thou'st made the world too beautiful this year.
My soul is all but out of me,—let fall
No burning leaf; prithee, let no bird call.

EDNA ST. VINCENT MILLAY

49

GREEN RAIN

Into the scented woods we'll go
And see the blackthorn swim in snow.
High above, in the budding leaves,
A brooding dove awakes and grieves;
The glades with mingled music stir,
And wildly laughs the woodpecker.
When blackthorn petals pearl the breeze,

There are the twisted hawthorn trees
Thick-set with buds, as clear and pale
As golden water or green hail—
As if a storm of rain had stood
Enchanted in the thorny wood,
And, hearing fairy voices call,
Hung poised, forgetting how to fall.

MARY WEBB

LOVELIEST OF TREES

Loveliest of trees, the cherry now
Is hung with bloom along the bough,
And stands about the woodland ride
Wearing white for Eastertide.

Now, of my threescore years and ten,
Twenty will not come again,
And take from seventy springs a score,
It only leaves me fifty more.

And since to look at things in bloom
Fifty springs are little room,
About the woodlands I will go
To see the cherry hung with snow.

A. E. Housman

DAFFODILS

... Daffodils
That come before the swallow dares, and take
The winds of March with beauty.

WILLIAM SHAKESPEARE

TO VIOLETS

Welcome, maids of honor,
    You do bring
    In the Spring,
And wait upon her.
She has virgins many,
    Fresh and fair;
    Yet you are
More sweet than any.

You're the maiden posies,
    And, so graced,
    To be placed
'Fore damask roses.
Yet, though thus respected,
    By and by
    Ye do lie,
Poor girls, neglected.

ROBERT HERRICK

SPRING

Spring, the sweet Spring, is the year's pleasant king;
Then blooms each thing, then maids dance in a ring;
Cold doth not sting, the pretty birds do sing,
Cuckoo, jug-jug, pu-we, to-witta-woo!

The palm and the may make country houses gay,
Lambs frisk and play, the shepherds pipe all day,
And we hear aye birds tune this merry lay,
Cuckoo, jug-jug, pu-we, to-witta-woo.

The fields breathe sweet, the daisies kiss our feet,
Young lovers meet, old wives a-sunning sit,
In every street these tunes our ears do greet,
Cuckoo, jug-jug, pu-we, to-witta-woo!
    Spring, the sweet Spring.

THOMAS NASH

A CHARM FOR SPRING FLOWERS

Who sees the first marsh marigold
Shall count more wealth than hands can hold.

Who bends a knee where violets grow
A hundred secret things shall know.

Who finds hepatica's dim blue
Shall have his dearest wish come true.

Who spies on lady-slippers fair
Shall keep a heart as light as air.

But whosoever toucheth not
One petal, sets no root in pot,

He shall be blessed of earth and sky
Till under them he, too, shall lie.

RACHEL FIELD

SONG

The year's at the spring,
And day's at the morn;
Morning's at seven;
The hillside's dew-pearled;
The lark's on the wing;
The snail's on the thorn;
God's in his heaven—
All's right with the world.

ROBERT BROWNING

Under the greenwood tree,
Who loves to lie with me,
And tune his merry note
Unto the sweet bird's throat,
Come hither, come hither, come hither;
    Here shall we see
    No enemy
But winter and rough weather.

Who doth ambition shun,
And loves to lie in the sun,
Seeking the food he eats,
And pleased with what he gets,
Come hither, come hither, come hither;
    Here shall he see
    No enemy
But winter and rough weather.

WILLIAM SHAKESPEARE

A HAWTHORN BERRY

How sweet a thought,
How strange a deed,
To house such glory in a seed—
A berry, shining rufously,
Like scarlet coral in the sea!
A berry, rounder than a ring,
So round, it harbors everything;
So red, that all the blood of men
Could never paint it so again.
And, as I hold it in my hand,
A fragrance steals across the land:
Rich, on the wintry heaven, I see
A white, immortal hawthorn-tree.

MARY WEBB

DAFFODILS

I wandered lonely as a cloud
That floats on high o'er vales and hills,
When all at once I saw a crowd—
A host, of golden daffodils,
Beside the lake, beneath the trees,
Fluttering and dancing in the breeze.

Continuous as the stars that shine
And twinkle on the Milky Way,
They stretched in never-ending line
Along the margin of a bay:
Ten thousand saw I, at a glance,
Tossing their heads in sprightly dance.

The waves beside them danced, but they
Out–did the sparkling waves in glee;
A poet could not but be gay
In such a jocund company;
I gazed and gazed—but little thought
What wealth the show to me had brought.

For oft, when on my couch I lie,
In vacant or in pensive mood,
They flash upon that inward eye
Which is the bliss of solitude,
And then my heart with pleasure fills,
And dances with the daffodils.

WILLIAM WORDSWORTH

WRITTEN IN MARCH

The cock is crowing,
The stream is flowing,
The small birds twitter,
The lake doth glitter,
    The green field sleeps in the sun;
The oldest and the youngest
Are at work with the strongest;
The cattle are grazing,
Their heads never raising;
    There are forty feeding like one!

Like an army defeated
The snow hath retreated
And now doth fare ill
On the top of the bare hill;
    The plough-boy is whooping anon, anon,
There's joy in the mountains;
There's life in the fountains;
Small clouds are sailing,
Blue sky prevailing;
    The rain is over and gone!

WILLIAM WORDSWORTH

THE FOUR SWEET MONTHS

First, April, she with mellow showers
Opens the way for early flowers;
Then after her comes smiling May,
In a more sweet and rich array;

Next enters June, and brings us more
Gems than those two that went before;
Then, lastly, July comes and she
More wealth brings in than all those three.

ROBERT HERRICK

69

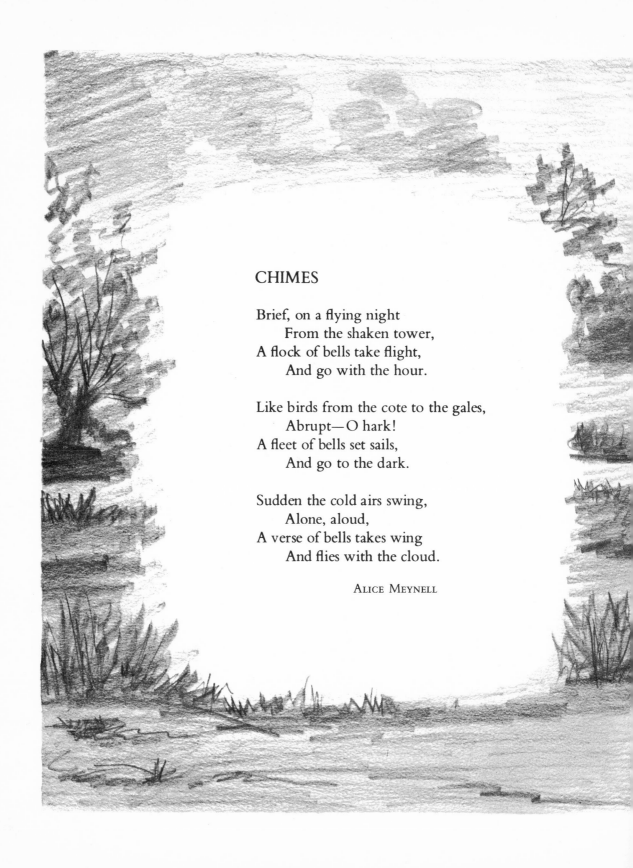

CHIMES

Brief, on a flying night
    From the shaken tower,
A flock of bells take flight,
    And go with the hour.

Like birds from the cote to the gales,
    Abrupt—O hark!
A fleet of bells set sails,
    And go to the dark.

Sudden the cold airs swing,
    Alone, aloud,
A verse of bells takes wing
    And flies with the cloud.

ALICE MEYNELL

THE NIGHT WILL NEVER STAY

The night will never stay,
The night will still go by,
Though with a million stars
You pin it to the sky;
Though you bind it with the blowing wind
And buckle it with the moon,
The night will slip away
Like a sorrow or a tune.

ELEANOR FARJEON

AUTUMN

The morns are meeker than they were,
    The nuts are getting brown;
The berry's cheek is plumper,
    The rose is out of town.

The maple wears a gayer scarf,
    The field a scarlet gown.
Lest I should be old-fashioned,
    I'll put a trinket on.

EMILY DICKINSON

When icicles hang on the wall,
    And Dick the Shepherd blows his nail,
And Tom bears logs into the hall,
    And milk comes frozen home in pail;
When blood is nipt and ways be foul,
Then nightly sings the staring owl
                     Tuwhoo!
Tuwhit! tuwhoo! A merry note!
While greasy Joan doth keel the pot.

When all around the wind doth blow,
    And coughing drowns the parson's saw,
And birds sit brooding in the snow
    And Marian's nose looks red and raw,
When roasted crabs hiss in the bowl,
Then nightly sings the staring owl
                    Tuwhoo!
Tuwhit! tuwhoo! A merry note
While greasy Joan doth keel the pot.

WILLIAM SHAKESPEARE

Cold winter now is in the wood,
The moon wades deep in snow.
Pile balsam boughs about the sills,
And let the fires glow!

The cows must stand in the dark barn,
The horses stamp all day.
Now shall the housewife bake her pies
And keep her kitchen gay.

The cat sleeps warm beneath the stove,
The dog on paws outspread;
But the brown deer with flinching hide
Seeks for a sheltered bed.

The fox steps hungry through the brush,
The lean hawk coasts the sky.
"Winter is in the wood!" the winds
In the warm chimney cry.

ELIZABETH COATSWORTH

For, lo, the winter is past,
The rain is over and gone;
The flowers appear on the earth;
The time of the singing of birds is come,
And the voice of the turtle is heard in our land.

THE SONG OF SONGS, 2:11, 12

Birds of the Air

Beasts of the Field

THE EAGLE

He clasps the crag with crooked hands;
Close to the sun in lonely lands,
Ringed with the azure world, he stands.

The wrinkled sea beneath him crawls;
He watches from his mountain walls,
And like a thunderbolt he falls.

ALFRED, LORD TENNYSON

"DUCKS' DITTY"

All along the backwater,
Through the rushes tall,
Ducks are a–dabbling,
Up tails all!

Ducks' tails, drakes' tails,
Yellow feet a–quiver,
Yellow bills all out of sight
Busy in the river!

Slushy green undergrowth
Where the roach swim—
Here we keep our larder,
Cool and full and dim.

Every one for what he likes!
We like to be
Heads down, tails up,
Dabbling free!

High in the blue above
Swifts whirl and call—
We are down a-dabbling
Up tails all!

KENNETH GRAHAME

CHANTICLEER

Of all the birds from East to West
    That tuneful are and dear,
I love that farmyard bird the best,
    They call him Chanticleer.

Gold plume and copper plume,
    Comb of scarlet gay;
'Tis he that scatters night and gloom,
    And summons back the day!

He is the sun's brave herald
    Who, ringing his blithe horn,
Calls round a world dew-pearled
    The heavenly airs of morn.

Oh, clear gold, shrill and bold,
    He calls through creeping mist
The mountains from the night and cold
    To rose and amethyst.

He sets the birds to singing,
    And calls the flowers to rise;
The morning cometh, bringing
    Sweet sleep to heavy eyes.

Gold plume and silver plume,
    Comb of coral gay;
'Tis he packs off the night and gloom,
    And summons home the day.

Black fear he sends it flying,
    Black care he drives afar;
And creeping shadows sighing
    Before the morning star.

The birds of all the forest
    Have dear and pleasant cheer,
But yet I hold the rarest
    The farmyard Chanticleer.

Red cock and black cock,
    Gold cock or white,
The flower of all the feathered flock,
    He summons back the light!

KATHERINE TYNAN

CROWS

I like to walk
And hear the black crows talk.

I like to lie
And watch crows sail the sky.

I like the crow
That wants the wind to blow:

I like the one
That thinks the wind is fun.

I like to see
Crows spilling from a tree,

And try to find
The top crow left behind.

I like to hear
Crows caw that spring is near.

I like the great
Wild clamor of crow hate

Three farms away
When owls are out by day.

I like the slow
Tired homeward-flying crow;

I like the sight
Of crows for my good night.

DAVID McCORD

THE OWL

When cats run home and light is come,
    And dew is cold upon the ground,
And the far-off stream is dumb,
    And the whirring sail goes round,
    And the whirring sail goes round:
        Alone and warming his five wits,
        The white owl in the belfry sits.

When merry milkmaids click the latch,
    And rarely smells the new-mown hay,
And the cock hath sung beneath the thatch
    Twice or thrice his roundelay,
    Twice or thrice his roundelay:
        Alone and warming his five wits,
        The white owl in the belfry sits.

ALFRED, LORD TENNYSON

THE LAST WORD OF A BLUEBIRD
(As Told to a Child)

As I went out a Crow
In a low voice said 'Oh,
I was looking for you.
How do you do?
I just came to tell you
To tell Lesley (will you?)
That her little Bluebird
Wanted me to bring word
That the north wind last night
That made the stars bright

And made ice on the trough
Almost made him cough
His tail feathers off.
He just had to fly!
But he sent her Good-by,
And said to be good,
And wear her red hood,
And look for skunk tracks
In the snow with an ax—
And do everything!
And perhaps in the spring
He would come back and sing.'

ROBERT FROST

THE WATER OUSEL

Where on the wrinkled stream the willows lean,
And fling a very ecstasy of green
Down the dim crystal, and the chestnut tree
Admires her large-leaved shadow, swift and free
A water ousel came, with such a flight
As archangels might envy. Soft and bright,
Upon a water-kissing bough she lit
And washed and preened her silver breast, though it
Was dazzling fair before. Then twittering
She sang, and made obeisance to the Spring.
And in the wavering amber at her feet
Her silent shadow, with obedience meet,
Made her quick, imitative curtsies too.
Maybe she dreamed a nest, so safe, so dear,
Where the keen spray leaps whitely to the weir;
And smooth warm eggs that hold a mystery;
And stirrings of life, and twitterings that she
Is passionately glad of; and a breast
As silver white as hers, which without rest
Or languor, borne by spread wings swift and strong,
Shall fly upon her service all day long.

She hears a presage in the ancient thunder
Of the silken fall, and her small soul in wonder
Makes preparation as she deems most right,
Re-purifying what before was white
Against the day when, like a beautiful dream,
Two little ousels shall fly with her down-stream,
And even the poor, dumb shadow-bird shall flit
With two small shadows following after it.

MARY WEBB

THE HENS

The night was coming very fast;
It reached the gate as I ran past.

The pigeons had gone to the tower of the church
And all the hens were on their perch,

Up in the barn, and I thought I heard
A piece of a little purring word.

I stopped inside, waiting and staying,
To try to hear what the hens were saying.

They were asking something, that was plain,
Asking it over and over again.

One of them moved and turned around,
Her feathers made a ruffled sound,

A ruffled sound, like a bushful of birds,
And she said her little asking words.

She pushed her head close into her wing,
But nothing answered anything.

ELIZABETH MADOX ROBERTS

THE HARE

In the black furrow of a field
I saw an old witch-hare this night;
And she cocked a lissome ear,
And she eyed the moon so bright,
And she nibbled of the green;
And I whispered "Whsst! witch-hare,"
Away like a ghostie o'er the field
She fled, and left the moonlight there.

WALTER DE LA MARE

STARLINGS

When the blue summer night
Is short and safe and light,
How should the starlings any more remember
The fearful, trembling times of dark December?
They mimic in their glee,
With impudent jocosity,
The terrible ululation of the owls
That prey
On just such folk as they.
"Tu-whoo!" And rusty-feathered fledglings, pressed
Close in the nest

Amid the chimney-stacks, are good all day
If their indulgent father will but play
At owls,
With predatory howls
And hoots and shrieks and whistlings wild and dread.
Says one small bird,
With lids drawn up, cosily tucked in bed,
"Such things were never heard
By me or you.
They are not true!"

MARY WEBB

THE RABBIT

When they said the time to hide was mine,
I hid back under a thick grape vine.

And while I was still for the time to pass,
A little gray thing came out of the grass.

He hopped his way through the melon bed
And sat down close by a cabbage head.

He sat down close where I could see,
And his big still eyes looked hard at me,

His big eyes bursting out of the rim,
And I looked back very hard at him.

ELIZABETH MADOX ROBERTS

A bird came down the walk:
He did not know I saw;
He bit an angle-worm in halves
And ate the fellow, raw.

And then he drank a dew
From a convenient grass,
And then hopped sidewise to the wall
To let a beetle pass.

EMILY DICKINSON

A BLACKBIRD SUDDENLY

Heaven is in my hand, and I
Touch a heart-beat of the sky,
Hearing a blackbird's cry.

Strange, beautiful, unquiet thing,
Lone flute of God, how can you sing
Winter to spring?

You have outdistanced every voice and word,
And given my spirit wings until it stirred
Like you—a bird!

JOSEPH AUSLANDER

SOMETHING TOLD THE WILD GEESE

Something told the wild geese
    It was time to go.
Though the fields lay golden
    Something whispered, "Snow."
Leaves were green and stirring,
    Berries, luster-glossed,
But beneath warm feathers
    Something cautioned, "Frost."

All the sagging orchards
    Steamed with amber spice,
But each wild breast stiffened
    At remembered ice.
Something told the wild geese
    It was time to fly—
Summer sun was on their wings,
    Winter in their cry.

RACHEL FIELD

THE TIGER

Tiger! Tiger! burning bright
In the forests of the night,
What immortal hand or eye
Could frame thy fearful symmetry?

In what distant deeps or skies
Burnt the fire of thine eyes?
On what wings dare he aspire?
What the hand dare seize the fire?

And what shoulder, and what art,
Could twist the sinews of thy heart?
And when thy heart began to beat,
What dread hand? and what dread feet?

What the hammer? what the chain?
In what furnace was thy brain?
What the anvil? what dread grasp
Dare its deadly terrors clasp?

When the stars threw down their spears,
And watered heaven with their tears,
Did He smile His work to see?
Did He who made the Lamb make thee?

Tiger! Tiger! burning bright
In the forests of the night,
What immortal hand or eye
Dare frame thy fearful symmetry?

WILLIAM BLAKE

Nonsense

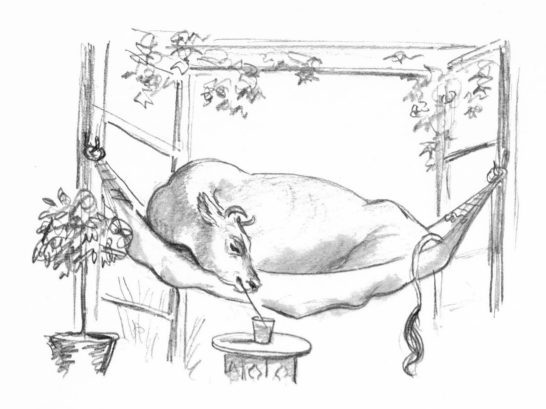

A NONSENSE SONG

Rosemary, Rosemary, let down your hair!
The cow's in the hammock, the crow's in the chair!
I was making you songs out of sawdust and silk,
But they came in to call and they spilt them like milk.

The cat's in the coffee, the wind's in the east,
He screams like a peacock and whines like a priest
And the saw of his voice makes my blood turn to mice—
So let down your long hair and shut off his advice!

Pluck out the thin hairpins and let the waves stream,
Brown-gold as brook-waters that dance through a dream,
Gentle-curled as young cloudlings, sweet-fragrant as bay,
Till it takes all the fierceness of living away.

Oh, when you are with me, my heart is white steel.
But the bat's in the belfry, the mold's in the meal,
And I think I hear skeletons climbing the stair!
—Rosemary, Rosemary, let down your bright hair!

STEPHEN VINCENT BENÉT

CALICO PIE

Calico pie,
      The little birds fly
      Down to the calico-tree:
Their wings were blue,
And they sang "Tilly-loo!"
Till away they flew;
    And they never came back to me!
      They never came back,
      They never came back,
    They never came back to me!

Calico jam,
      The little Fish swam
Over the Syllabub Sea.
      He took off his hat
      To the Sole and the Sprat,
      And the Willeby-wat;
But he never came back to me!
      He never came back,
      He never came back,
He never came back to me!

Calico ban,
The little Mice ran
To be ready in time for tea;
Flippity flup,
They drank it all up,
And danced in the cup;
But they never came back to me!
They never came back,
They never came back,
They never came back to me!

Calico drum,
The Grasshoppers come,
The Butterfly, Beetle, and Bee,
Over the ground,
Around and round,
With a hop and a bound;
But they never came back!
They never came back,
They never came back,
They never came back to me!

EDWARD LEAR

REBECCA
Who Slammed Doors for Fun and Perished Miserably

A Trick that everyone abhors
In Little Girls is slamming Doors.
A Wealthy Banker's little Daughter
Who lived in Palace Green, Bayswater
(By name Rebecca Offendort),
Was given to this Furious Sport.
She would deliberately go
And Slam the door like Billy-Ho!
To make her Uncle Jacob start.
She was not really bad at heart,
But only rather rude and wild;
She was an Aggravating Child.

It happened that a Marble Bust
Of Abraham was standing just
Above the Door this little Lamb
Had carefully prepared to Slam,
And down it came! It knocked her flat!
It laid her out! She looked like that!

Her Funeral Sermon (which was long
And followed by a Sacred Song)
Mentioned her Virtues, it is true,
But dwelt upon her Vices, too,
And showed the Dreadful End of One
Who goes and slams the Door for Fun.

HILAIRE BELLOC

MR. LEAR

"How pleasant to know Mr. Lear!"
    Who has written such volumes of stuff!
Some think him ill-tempered and queer,
    But a few think him pleasant enough.

His mind is concrete and fastidious,
    His nose is remarkably big;
His visage is more or less hideous,
    His beard it resembles a wig.

He has ears, and two eyes, and ten fingers,
    Leastways if you reckon two thumbs;
Long ago he was one of the singers,
    But now he is one of the dumbs.

He sits in a beautiful parlor,
    With hundreds of books on the wall;
He drinks a great deal of Marsala,
    But never gets tipsy at all.

He has many friends, laymen and clerical,
    Old Foss is the name of his cat.
His body is perfectly spherical,
    He weareth a runcible hat.

When he walks in a waterproof white,
    The children run after him so!
Calling out, "He's come out in his night-
    gown, that crazy old Englishman, oh!"

He weeps by the side of the ocean,
    He weeps on the top of the hill;
He purchases pancake and lotion,
    And chocolate shrimps from the mill.

He reads but he cannot speak Spanish,
    He cannot abide ginger-beer:
Ere the days of his pilgrimage vanish,
    How pleasant to know Mr. Lear!

EDWARD LEAR